This amazing book belongs to

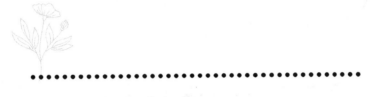

....

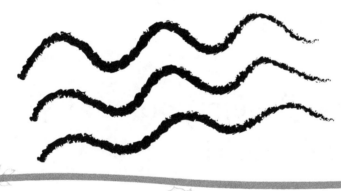

TABLE OF CONTENTS

WORD SEARCH

Stimulate your brain with a classic game of Word Search! Word Search is a game composed of the letters of words formatted in a grid. The goal is to find all of the words hidden in the puzzle. Find all the words from the themed word list in the puzzle grid. Words may be found going forwards, backwards, up, down or diagonally. Word Searches are not only a great way to pass the time, but also provide a great exercise for keeping your brain fit.

MAZES

A maze is a puzzle with twists and turns, where you try to find a path from the entrance to the exit without hitting dead ends. You can help your pet to find his way to the other side. The goal of a maze is to get through it, which means going the wrong way, retracing your steps, and choosing different paths.

MATH PUZZLE

Math doesn't have to be boring. Math puzzle is one of the best and oldest ways to encourage student engagement.

Sharing these fun puzzles with your kids is a great way to get them thinking mathematically and solving problems in a fun and engaging way! It's so simple, you just have to find the missing number and place it in the correct box

WHAT AM I?

Can you guess what I am from the description? Let me tell you something about myself. Then see if you can guess what I am. and fill in your crossword "across" and "down"

WORD SCRAMBLE!

The goal of this is to unscramble the list of letters found at the bottom of the page, and find the correct word ((countries of the world, national capitals, fruits and vegetables names and furniture names)

COLORING SECTION!

with our beautiful coloring collection, your kid can have a little of mind peace after all the hard work!

Enjoy!

CHAPTER 1
Name your pets (Word Search)

- Find the dogs names

S	U	Y	T	M	A	X	R
A	N	B	P	Z	R	Y	R
B	Y	O	C	O	C	D	R
Z	D	T	S	U	H	D	F
C	D	I	L	O	I	U	V
Z	E	A	L	L	E	B	H
Z	T	I	F	F	S	Q	X
F	M	M	D	V	E	N	I

- ARCHIE
- BELLA
- BUDDY
- COCO
- LUCY

- MAX
- MILO
- ROSIE
- TEDDY
- TOBY

- Now you can colore your dog

- Chose a nice name for your dog

. . . .

- *Find the cats names*

R	E	V	I	L	O	T	C
T	I	G	E	R	L	H	S
F	L	U	F	F	Y	O	Y
Y	X	H	Q	A	P	M	L
A	S	Q	H	H	A	A	L
M	X	S	I	A	P	S	I
P	A	E	I	C	C	W	L
S	O	S	O	M	Z	I	G

- **FLUFFY**
- **GIZMO**
- **LILLY**
- **MISSY**
- **OLIVER**

- **SAM**
- **SASHA**
- **SOPHIE**
- **THOMAS**
- **TIGER**

- *Now you can colore your cat*

- *Chose a nice name for your cat*

....

- *Find the rabbits names*

R Y W S R U C Y
E B I N P M K O
P A G O R N R Y
M B G W I E A Z
U U L B O P N G
H N E A V Z G U
T N S L Z U E B
R E V L I S L I

- ANGEL
- BABY
- BINKY
- BUGZY
- BUNN
- OREO
- SILVER
- SNOWBALL
- THUMPER
- WIGGLES

- *Now you can colore your rabbit*

- *Chose a nice name for your rabbit*

....

- Find the hamster names

D	R	A	G	O	N	S	G
L	C	H	E	W	Y	E	O
E	F	C	E	J	I	R	R
S	E	D	I	N	E	E	D
N	L	H	N	X	T	X	O
A	I	A	R	X	K	Z	N
H	X	T	E	L	M	A	H
D	E	D	B	I	C	I	O

- ANNIE
- BERNIE
- CHEWY
- DEXTER
- DRAGON

- FELIX
- GORDON
- HAMLET
- HANSEL
- REX

- Now you can colore your hamster

- Chose a nice name for your hamster

....

- *Find the birds names*

```
Z R T W E E T Y
R N E I W Y D S
E Y U T E Q C I
K O H N S R W V
O D R A N O E L
J A T I N Y O E
B C A S P E R R
T U N A E P R Y
```

• **BARNEY**	• **PEANUT**
• **CASPER**	• **ROOSTER**
• **ELVIS**	• **TINY**
• **JOKER**	• **TWEETY**
• **LEONARDO**	• **YODA**

- *Now you can colore your bird*

- *Chose a nice name for your bird*

....

- *Find the turtles names*

• **BRUNO**	• **PETUNIA**
• **CAMO**	• **SQUIRT**
• **DORIS**	• **STARLA**
• **GLORIA**	• **TINA**
• **NAPOLEON**	• **TONY**

```
N A P O L E O N
P P J O F G S S
O E M O L J Q I
M A T O N P U R
C I R U M U I O
X I T O N Y R D
A D O A N I T B
A L R A T S A T
```

- *Now you can colore your turtle*

- *Chose a nice name for your turtle*

....

- Find the fishs names

B	K	R	A	K	E	N	C
W	U	B	L	U	E	R	A
O	A	B	Y	Z	Y	A	P
D	C	Y	B	S	T	E	T
A	J	L	T	L	N	G	A
H	H	A	E	N	E	N	I
S	L	D	Y	O	S	S	N
E	N	U	T	P	E	N	L

- **BRUNO**
- **CAMO**
- **DORIS**
- **GLORIA**
- **NAPOLEON**

- **PETUNIA**
- **SQUIRT**
- **STARLA**
- **TINA**
- **TONY**

- Now you can colore your fish

- Chose a nice name for your fish

....

- Find the chameleons names

E	O	L	I	V	I	A	S
L	I	X	C	B	O	Y	U
I	O	L	W	O	A	B	M
Z	W	A	R	E	B	E	I
Z	E	I	L	A	L	R	X
Y	O	A	K	O	H	T	A
Z	Z	Y	N	D	K	C	M
A	L	L	I	Z	D	O	G

- **AZALEA**   - **LIZZY**
- **CHARLIE**   - **MAXIMUS**
- **COBRA**   - **MELON**
- **GODZILLA**   - **OLIVIA**
- **KIWI**   - **ZOE**

- Now you can colore chameleon

- Chose a nice name for your chameleon

....

- Find the ducks names

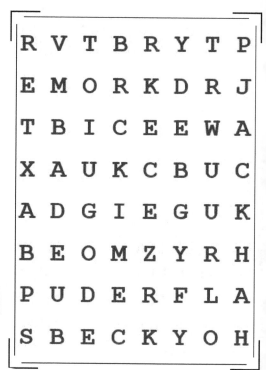

R	V	T	B	R	Y	T	P
E	M	O	R	K	D	R	J
T	B	I	C	E	E	W	A
X	A	U	K	C	B	U	C
A	D	G	I	E	G	U	K
B	E	O	M	Z	Y	R	H
P	U	D	E	R	F	L	A
S	B	E	C	K	Y	O	H

- ALFRED
- BAXTER
- BECKY
- BOB
- DUCKY
- HUBERT
- JACK
- MIKEY
- MOE
- PRECIOUS

- Now you can colore your duck

- Chose a nice name for your duck

....

- Find the chickens names

E	G	H	E	Y	R	T	T
G	S	A	G	T	E	A	R
G	B	Z	G	S	K	C	A
H	U	E	S	U	A	O	H
E	Z	L	T	R	E	D	G
A	A	K	E	S	B	D	G
D	Z	V	I	U	Y	X	E
B	L	A	N	C	A	S	H

- BEAKER
- BETSY
- BLANCA
- EGGHART
- EGGHEAD
- EGGSTEIN
- HAZEL
- RUSTY
- TACO
- ZAZU

- Now you can colore your chicken

- Chose a nice name for your chicken

....

CHAPTER 2
help your pet to find his way (mazes)

- Help Mr. Horse to find his way to the stable

- You did alright! now it's coloring time!

- One of the chicks is missing, help the mom to find 'em

- You did alright! now it's coloring time!

- Oh no! the nasty wolf is coming! help!!!

- Great you did it! now you can color it

- Help the farmer to get to the chicken nest

- Great! now we can make some delicious omelet !

- Help Mr Turkey to get to the farme

- Okay! See what he brought for us

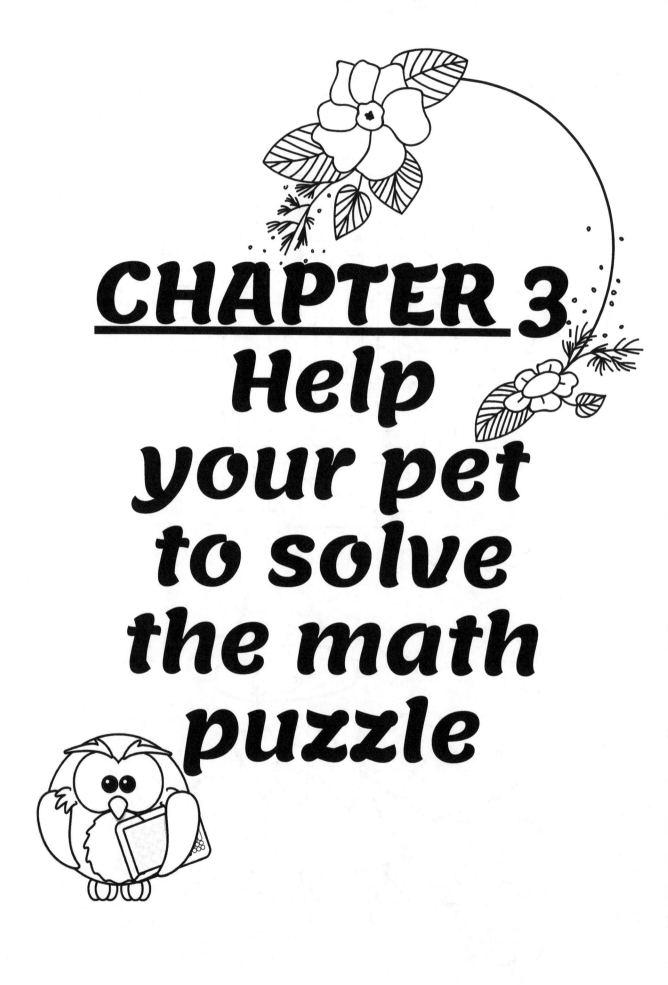

CHAPTER 3
Help your pet to solve the math puzzle

- Help Mr. Owl to solve this math puzzle

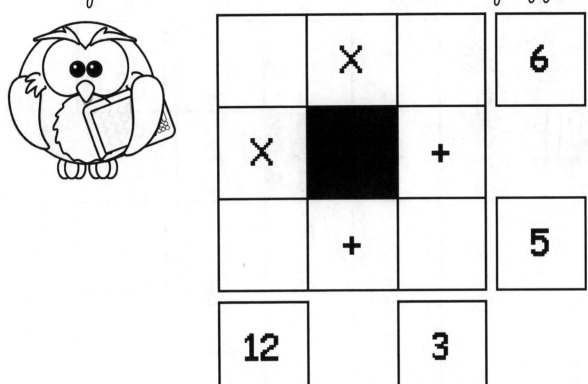

- Great! You did it well! Now you can connect the stars

- Help Mrs. Cow to solve this math puzzle

	-		1
-	■	+	
	-		1
-2	4		

- Great! You did it well! Now you can connect the stars

- Help Mr. Snake to solve this math puzzle

	-	
x	■	+
	-	

-1

1

6

5

- Great! You did it well! Now you can connect the dots

- Help the Unicorn to solve this math puzzle

	+		**4**
+	■	+	
	+		**6**
5		**5**	

- Great! You did it well! Now you can connect the dots

CHAPTER 4
What am I? (guss game)

What am I!

- Fill in your crossword!

Down

1. You use me in art class.

2. Don't touch me with anything sharp.

Across

3. I am a safe ride.

4. I have many doors and windows.

5. I transport heavy loads

What am I?

- Fill in your crossword!

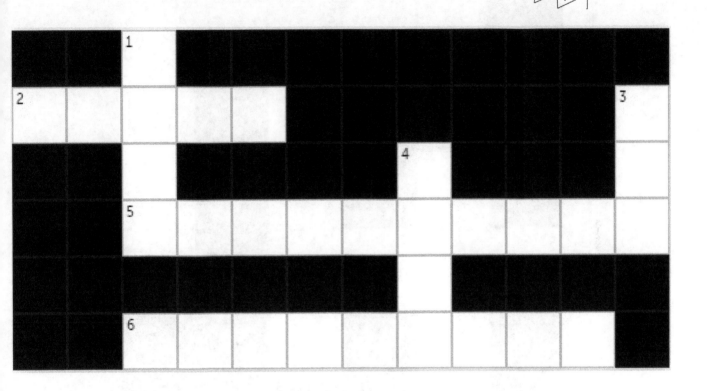

Down

1. Tie me up when you're done.

3. I disappear in the night

4. I am an easy pet to look after

Across

2. Don't go outside without me

5. I plug into the wall

6. I can connect you to the world

What am I?

- Fill in your crossword!

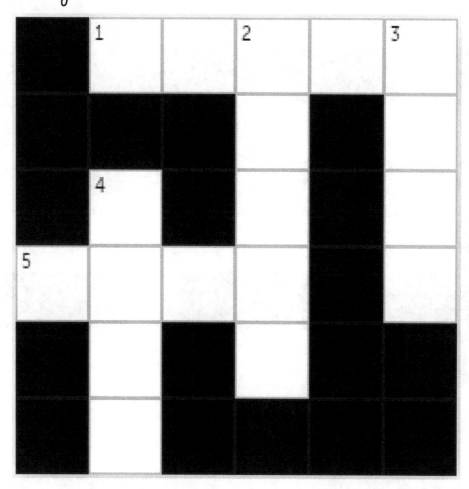

Down

2. I am a healthy snack.

3. I'm a house for a bird.

4. I cry a lot.

Across

1. I am the symbol for love.

5. I go up and down.

What am I?

- Fill in your crossword!

Down

2. I play in your vegetable garden.

3. I smell nice.

4. I will light your way.

Across

1. You need a key for me.

5. I am a home for royalty

What am I!

- Fill in your crossword!

Down

1. Run if you want me to fly faster.

4. I'll protect you from a cold wind.

Across

2. I appear after a storm.

3. One of my flavours is vanilla.

What am I?

- Fill in your crossword!

Down

1. I'm a curious creature.

2. I get colder as you go higher.

3. I'll keep your hair dry.

Across

4. Hug me if you have a bad dream.

5. Fighting with me is fun.

CHAPTER 5
Word scramble!

Word scramble

● Countries of the World

Hints

1. NACHI
2. ERNAIIG
3. AZLBIR
4. DNNGALE
5. RSASUI
6. JNAAP
7. TGPEY
8. EVTINMA
9. YGNMARE

Word scramble

1							
2							
3							
4							
5							
6							
7							
8							
9							

● National capitals

Hints

1. AMLI
2. DOLNON
3. MDDAIR
4. OATAWT
5. RSAIP

6. EORM
7. LSEOU
8. NARKAA
9. AADHBGD

Word scramble

1					
2					
3					
4					
5					
6					
7					
8					
9					

- Fruits and Vegetables names

Hints

1. TAOOTM
2. NAAANB
3. PAAAYP
4. ONMEL
5. LNOME

6. CONR
7. TPTOAO
8. NOINO
9. SDARHI

Word scramble

1						
2						
3						
4						
5						
6						
7						
8						
9						

● Furniture names

Hints

1. NHEBC
2. BFFUTE
3. EDB
4. AEST
5. AFSO

6. LTABE
7. RIMROEA
8. CIHRA
9. EKSD

Word scramble

1	

• Vehicles names

Hints

1. AVN
2. ITXA
3. STREOOC
4. BYAUSW
5. TINRA

6. USB
7. ECANR
8. BTAO
9. EYIBCCL

CHAPTER 6
Coloring Section!

Coloring Section

Coloring Section

Coloring Section

Coloring Section

Coloring Section

Coloring Section

Coloring Section